Trees are
the largest of all plants and
are the oldest known living things on
earth.   Some live for hundreds, even thousands
of years!   Trees provide shade and offer beautiful
areas for recreation.   They are homes to countless creatures in
the Animal Kingdom. Each spring, tree buds and flowers herald
the coming of warm weather. In fall, their leaves can be a kaleidoscope
of crayon colors. Some trees bear fruit and nuts and offer food for
people and other animals.   Thousands of different products come
from trees, too. Spices, lumber, paper, plastics, chocolate, medicines,
fuel, and rubber are just a few. And how could we have treehouses
without trees?   On a global scale, trees hold down topsoil, help prevent
flooding, and influence our climate. Tree leaves absorb carbon dioxide
from the air and release oxygen to make our air more breatheable.
There are about 20,000 different kinds of trees on the earth. This
book spotlights thirty of them.   Read and learn and act to
protect the trees that are here.   Plant new trees
for your children to enjoy.   And
always remember that we must
work together
to keep a
healthy
balance
of the
earth's
resources.
Trees are to
be treasured.
They are our
partners on this planet.

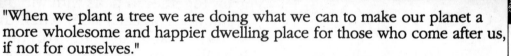

"When we plant a tree we are doing what we can to make our planet a
more wholesome and happier dwelling place for those who come after us,
if not for ourselves."

Oliver Wendell Holmes

Written By
Kathie Billingslea Smith
for Kevin, Ryan, Emily and
especially Bruce

Layout and Illustration By
MJ Studios, Inc.

The sugar maple, also known as the rock or hard maple, is the most valuable of all the maple trees. Its light reddish-brown lumber is sturdy and strong. This valuable hardwood is used to make furniture, cabinets, floors, boxes, musical instrument parts, and many other things. It also burns slowly and is an efficient fuel.

Sugar maples grow from Georgia north to Newfoundland, and from the east coast west to Texas and Manitoba. Reaching heights of 75 to 100 feet (22.5-30 m.), they make excellent shade trees. With gray, shaggy bark and broad dark leaves that grow in pairs opposite each other, sugar maples are known for their beauty. In autumn, the leaves change to brilliant orange, yellow, and red. The maple leaf is featured on the Canadian flag and is the official emblem of Canada. The sugar maple is the state tree of New York, Vermont, West Virginia, and Wisconsin.

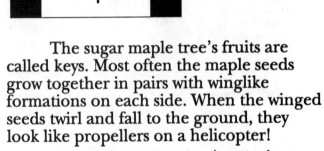

The sugar maple tree's fruits are called keys. Most often the maple seeds grow together in pairs with winglike formations on each side. When the winged seeds twirl and fall to the ground, they look like propellers on a helicopter!

In early spring, sugar maple trees are tapped so that the colorless, sugary sap can flow through holes in the trunks. The sap is collected and boiled to make maple syrup and maple sugar. Approximately 35 gallons (132 l.) of sap are needed to make one gallon (3.8 l.) of sweet, thick maple syrup. If the sap is allowed to boil beyond the syrup stage, it becomes maple sugar. Native Americans first showed English and French settlers how to do this. Today the production of maple syrup and sugar is a big business in Vermont, New York, Ontario, and especially Quebec.

OLDER BUCKET METHOD

TULIP TREE

The tulip tree, or tulip poplar, is a valuable source of hardwood and the tallest broadleaf tree in the eastern United States. It grows straight and tall and reaches heights of 80 to 200 feet (24-61 m.). Because its branches are far above the ground, it does not make a good shade tree, but is widely used as an ornamental.

The tulip tree is an ancient species. Leaf fossils fifty million years old have been found in Europe and Greenland. Today the tulip tree grows east of the Mississippi River and up to southern Ontario in Canada. It is the state tree of Indiana, Kentucky, and Tennessee.

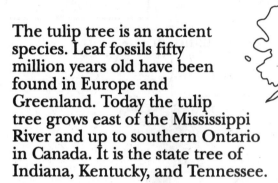

The tulip tree gets its name from the light green tulip-like flowers that bloom in late May or early June. Each flower develops into a 3-inch (7.5 cm.) cone-shaped fruit with small winged seeds clustered together. Birds and squirrels love to eat the seeds. The tree's leaves are smooth, broad and have notched tips. In fall, they turn a pretty yellow or orange color.

Underneath the tulip tree's rough, grayish-brown bark is white sapwood. The inner core of wood, or heartwood, is a light yellow color. The tulip tree is sometimes called the yellow poplar for this reason. This wood is straight-grained and easily worked. Years ago, Native Americans hollowed out canoes from tulip tree trunks. Today this valuable wood is used to make furniture, boats, boxes, baskets, and pulp.

FRUIT

AMERICAN BEECH

The American beech is a stately tree that tolerates shade and grows well in the rich soils of forests. It is found in the eastern half of the United States and southeastern Canada.

American beeches have smooth, gray bark and grow to be 60 to 80 feet (18-24 m.) tall. Their big roots spread out along the ground at the bases of the trees. Early in the spring, both male and female flowers bloom before the trees' thin, oval leaves are fully developed. In autumn, the leaves turn a deep golden color. The beech trees' fruits are small, triangular nuts that grow inside prickly burs. When the burs crack open, the nuts are eaten by woodland birds and animals. People enjoy them too.

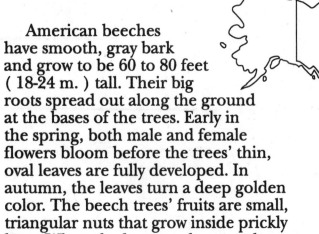

SEED

FRUIT

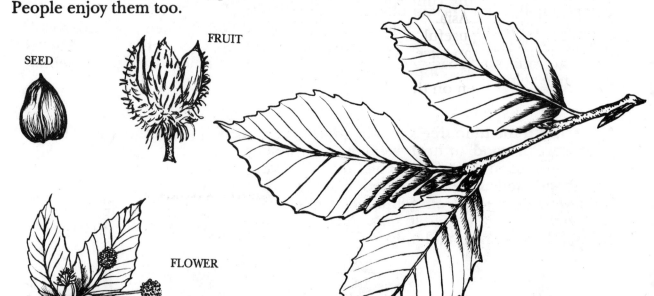

FLOWER

American beech wood is sturdy and close-grained. It is used to make barrels, wooden utensils, and furniture. This hardwood also burns slowly and is an excellent fuel.

In recent years, many of the beeches in New England have been attacked by a fungu. This disease may prove to be a serious problem.

Where would the sport of baseball be without ash trees? Almost all of the wooden baseball bats manufactured today are made from ash wood. This fine-grained, light-colored, strong, elastic wood is also used to make skis, boat oars, baskets, tool handles, musical instruments, and furniture. Ash wood is also an excellent fuel.

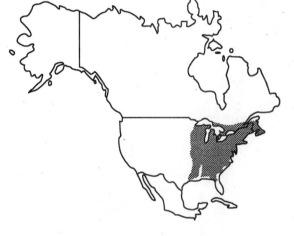

The white ash grows in southern Canada and the eastern half of the United States, with the exception of Florida. As many as twenty other kinds of ash trees are also found in the rest of the United States, Europe , and Asia. In addition to being useful, the white ash is also an excellent shade tree. It reaches heights of 60 to 90 feet (18.5-27 m.) and has compound leaves made up of seven oval leaflets. The leaflets are dark green on the top and silvery green underneath. In autumn, they turn a deep yellow or purplish color. Clusters of winged seeds shaped like canoe paddles and known as keys form in spring and drop off the tree in late fall. Then the white ash tree's bark, gray in color and with many fissures and ridges, can be easily seen.

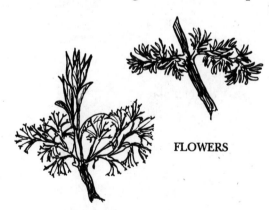

FLOWERS

FRUIT

The quaking aspen is a small to mid-sized tree in the poplar family. It grows quickly in sandy or rocky soils and burnt-over land, reaching heights of 20 to 40 feet (6-12 m.). Quaking aspens are found in the northeastern United States, in the Rocky Mountains, and all across Canada to Alaska. The trees' thin, smooth bark is greenish-white in color. The leaves, glossy green above and dull green beneath, are shaped like spades and arranged alternately on the twigs. In autumn, they turn a beautiful shade of golden yellow. Aspen seeds hang in a cone-shaped capsule. The wood of the aspen tree is used to make boxes, bowls, matches, and pulpwood for paper.

The quaking aspen if so named because its leaves flutter with the faintest breeze. Through the years, this characteristic has prompted many explanations and stories. According to Native American legend, the Great Spirit once visited the earth and saw a young aspen tree. The tree stood straight and tall and did not show respect by bowing down. As punishment, the Great Spirit decreed that all aspen trees would tremble in humility forever.

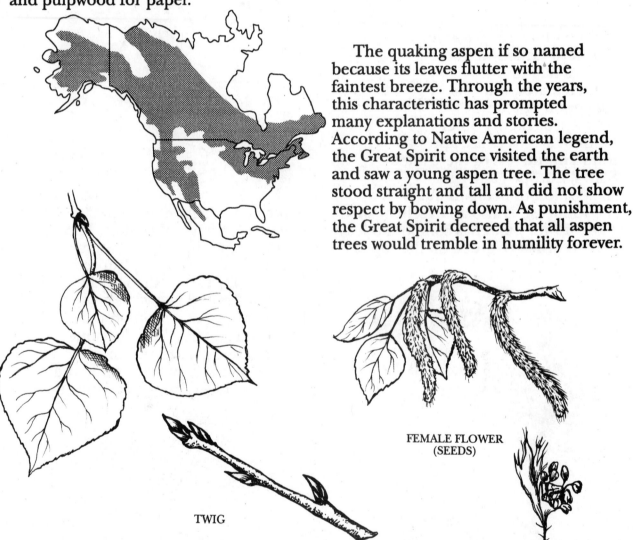

TWIG

FEMALE FLOWER
(SEEDS)

Another story claims that the aspen tree was used to make the cross on which Jesus was crucified. As a result, the story goes, the aspen tree trembles in fear and shame. Superstitious settlers on the American frontier believed this story and would not enter cabins made of aspen logs!

Scientists believe that the ginkgo tree may be the oldest of all tree species. More than 200 million years ago, Brachiosaurus, Apatosaurus, and other plant-eating dinosaurs probably munched on ginkgo leaves for lunch! Ancient fossils of ginkgo leaves have been found in many parts of the world. This slender, graceful tree also appealed to people. Long after the dinosaurs were gone, ginkgo trees were cultivated for hundreds of centuries in Chinese and Japanese temple gardens. The name ginkgo is a Japanese word. The tree's fernlike leaves are shaped like Japanese fans.

Today ginkgo trees are still largely used as ornamental trees and are found in many countries. They are often planted along city streets because ginkgos grow well even in polluted areas. They reach heights of 60 to 80 feet (18-24 m.). In autumn, ginkgo leaves turn a pretty shade of yellow and then abruptly fall from the trees. Ginkgo seeds have a hard nutlike center covered by a soft yellow outer covering that smells like rancid butter. Chinese and Japanese people remove the soft outer pulp and eat the ginkgo seeds. Only female trees bear the seeds. Many gardeners choose to plant the male form of the ginkgo which only grows pollen.

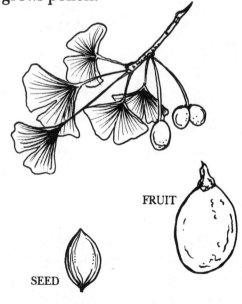

FRUIT

SEED

MESQUITE

Mesquite is a low-growing shrub found in the West Indies, western South America, the Hawaiian Islands, Mexico, and the southwestern United States. It does not need much water and thrives in hot, dry climates, even desert areas, where few other plants grow.

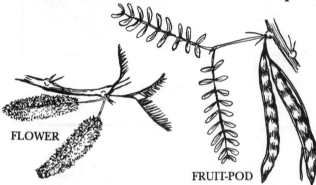

FLOWER

FRUIT-POD

When good water supplies are close by, the mesquite grows into a good-sized tree reaching a height of 20-50 feet (6-15 m.). The tree's roots can grow down as far as 60 feet (18 m.) to reach underground water sources!

Mesquite bark is light brown and ridged. Its leaves are compound with many little leaflets growing opposite each other on the stem. Long ago, Native American tribes of the southwestern United States ate mesquite seeds or beans. Mesquite wood is used to build buildings and fences. It also serves as a fuel and gives a pleasant taste to grilled foods.

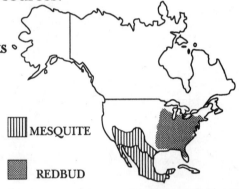

‖‖‖ MESQUITE

REDBUD

REDBUD

In early spring, the branches of the redbud tree erupt with masses of tiny one-inch (2.5 cm.) lavendar-pink flowers. It is a spectacular sight! Redbuds grow in southern Europe, Asia, Japan, and the eastern half of the United States. The tree itself has no commercial value, but it is a favorite ornamental tree for many people. It is the state tree of Oklahoma. The redbud grows well in rich, sandy soil and reaches heights of up to 40 feet (12 m.). The redbud tree is also known as the Judas Tree.

The smooth brown bark of the young redbud becomes ridged as the tree grows older. In autumn, its heart-shaped leaves turn bright yellow. Redbud seeds are housed in flat, thin pods that deer and other wild animals love to eat.

FLOWER

FRUIT-POD

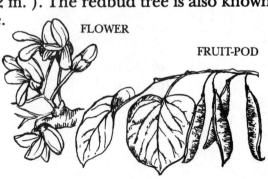

Apples have been a popular fruit for more then 2 1/2 million years. Charcoal apple remains have been found where European Stone Age villages once stood. During the Roman Empire, apple seeds were spread further throughout Europe. Later, English colonists brought apple seeds and apple trees to America. The trees spread rapidly across the continent as settlers moved west. The acres of apple orchards in Pennsylvania, Ohio, Illinois, and Indiana, covering over a hundred thousand square miles of land, were started partly through the efforts of Jonathan Chapman. Nicknamed "Johnny Appleseed," he wandered the countryside for almost fifty years, preaching and planting apple seeds wherever he went. Today apple trees are found all over the world except in areas of extreme heat or cold. More than two billion bushels of apples are produced each year worldwide! Approximately one-half of these are eaten fresh. The rest are used to make pies, apple juice, applesauce, apple butter, jelly, wine and many other things.

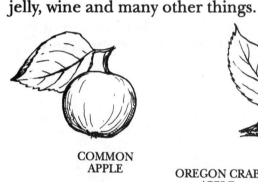

COMMON
APPLE

OREGON CRAB
APPLE

Apple trees grow to be 20-30 feet (6-9 m.) tall. Their oval-shaped leaves turn yellow or brown in the fall. Apple trees can bear fruit for as long as 100 years. However, most gardeners replace their orchard trees after about 50 years of service. Apple trees are members of the rose family. Each spring, pretty white flowers, resembling roses, bloom on the trees. Later an apple grows where each flower bloomed. Apples are harvested in late summer or early fall. Altogether there are thousands of different kinds of apples ranging from red to green to yellow in color and from tart to sweet in taste. More than half of the apples grown in the United States and Canada are Red Delicious, Golden Delicious, and McIntosh. Rome Beauty and Jonathan are two other popular types. Apples are the leading fruit crop grown in Canada.

FLOWER

WINTER BUD
OR SPUR

The paper birch, or white birch, is one of about forty different kinds of birch trees in the world. It is the state tree of New Hampshire and is found in Canada, the northern United States, and the Appalachian Mountains. Its smooth, chalk-white bark peels off the trunk in thin, broad sheets almost like paper. These sheets are strong, waterproof, and insectproof.

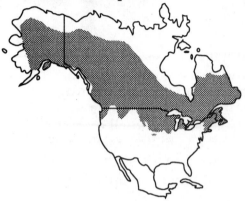

For years, Native Americans used paper birchbark to make wigwams and birchbark canoes.The birchbark sheets were strong enough to support the weight of several people and pliable enough to mold easily into the rounded shapes of the wigwam and canoe. Because of this distinction, the paper birch is sometimes called the canoe birch. Today Native Americans still use birchbark to make baskets and small ornaments.

BARK

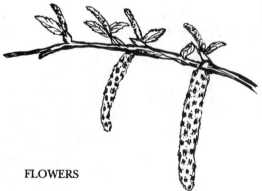

FLOWERS

Most paper birches grow to heights of 60 to 80 feet (18-24 m.). The trees' oval leaves are 2 to 4 inches (5-10 cm.) long with a dark green color on the top and lighter green underneath. Small, winged seeds are encased in thin cones that hang from the trees.

Paper birches are slender trees that grow best in open woods and along riverbanks. American poet Robert Frost loved birches and used the thin trunks to swing upon when he was a child. In his poem "Birches," he wrote longingly of those times.

Many people think that the American elm tree is shaped like an umbrella. Its open, spreading branches make it an excellent shade tree. American elms grow to be 75 to 100 feet (23-30 m.) tall and are found in the United States and southern Canada, east of the Rocky Mountains. Other elms grow in Europe, Asia, and northern Africa. They can live for as long as 200 years!

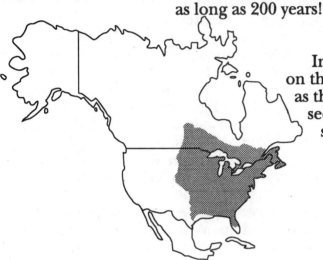

In early spring, little green flowers bloom on the elm tree before the leaves appear. Then as the leaves unfurl, the small, flat , winged seeds drop from the tree. Game birds, squirrels, and opossums love to eat them. Elm leaves are slightly lopsided and have double-toothed edges. They turn yellow and brown in the fall.

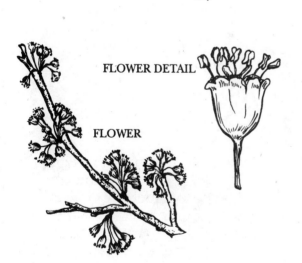

FLOWER DETAIL

FLOWER

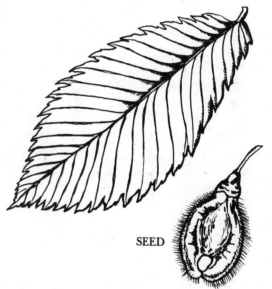

SEED

Years ago, Native Americans burned elm wood for fuel and used strong fibers from the elm trees' bark to make ropes. Today the trees' light brown hardwood is used to make furniture, barrels, fenceposts, and boats.

The American elm is the state tree of Massachusetts and North Dakota. Its future, however, is in jeopardy. Each year many elms are killed by the Dutch elm disease, a fungus spread by beetles. Stands of dead elm trees can be found in many places. Scientists are trying to halt the destruction of these beautiful trees.

Among the more than 600 types of oak trees, the white oak is one of the best known. It is found in the eastern half of the United States and is the state tree of Maryland, Illinois, and Connecticut. Other oaks grow throughout the United States, China, Japan, and parts of Europe.

When you walk through a forest of deciduous trees, the tallest, oldest trees around are probably oaks. White oaks grow very slowly, but eventually become sturdy, majestic trees of 60 to 120 feet (18-37 m.) in height. They live to be 200 to 400 years old. The trees' bark is light gray and scaly. In spring, small yellowish-green flowers form. Once fertilized, these flowers develop into large, pointy acorns. The acorns are the fruits of the oak tree and are eaten by squirrels, chipmunks, deer, and other woodland animals. In years past, Native Americans also included acorns in their diets. White oak leaves have five to nine rounded lobes. They turn red in autumn and light brown in winter.

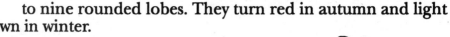

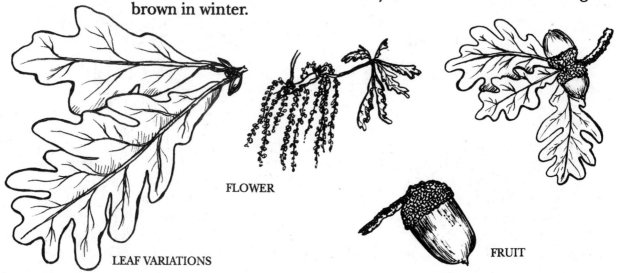

FLOWER

LEAF VARIATIONS

FRUIT

Oak wood is a strong, durable hardwood with a beautiful grain or pattern of growth. It is highly prized for lumber and is widely used to manufacture flooring, paneling, furniture, boats, and barrels. Oaks provide almost half the hardwood lumber produced in America each year. Oak wood also burns slowly and makes an excellent fuel.

AMERICAN CHESTNUT

American chestnut trees are excellent shade trees because of their wide-spreading branches. They grow to reach heights of 70-90 feet (21-27 m.) and have very rough, grayish-brown bark. The glossy, green leaves are long and slender. The tree is probably best known for its tasty chestnuts. The nuts are encased in a prickly bur and taste especially good when roasted.

NUT

BUR

FLOWER

American chestnut trees once grew all over the eastern United States. In the last fifty years, however, a fungus disease called chestnut blight destroyed most of them. Only a few scattered chestnut trees remain. Scientists are working to develop new blight-resistant strains.

Chestnut wood is very durable and was used to make railroad ties, telephone poles, fence posts, and furniture. The wood is so long-lasting that even dead trees are used for lumber.

FLOWERING DOGWOOD

Many different types of dogwood trees grow throughout the United States and Canada. Of these, the most common is the flowering, or American, dogwood. This pretty tree is found in the eastern United States. It is the state flower of North Carolina and Virginia and the provincial flower of British Columbia. It is also the state flower of Missouri and Virginia.

The flowering dogwood is a slow-growing tree that reaches heights of 10 to 40 feet (3-12 m.). It grows well in forest shade. Each spring when most other tree limbs are still bare, flowering dogwoods flash splashes of color throughout wooded areas. Wild dogwoods bear clusters of white flowers, and cultivated dogwoods have pink and white blooms. The leaves of the flowering dogwood are oval and pointed on the ends. In fall, they turn pretty shades of yellow, red and orange. The tree's fruits are bright red drupes that look like berries.They usually have two seeds. Birds eat dogwood fruits, and skunks, deer, and squirrels munch on the tree's twigs and bark.

FLOWER

FRUIT

Flowering dogwoods are grown primarily as ornamentals. The tree's hard, finely-grained wood, however, is used to make tool handles, golf club heads, and shuttles for weaving.

WILD BLACK CHERRY

Cherry trees are an ancient species that originated in Asia. From there, traders and explorers carried cherry seeds to all parts of Europe and then to America. Today there are many kinds of cultivated cherry trees, such as the ones decorating Washington D.C.. There are also about fourteen different species of wild cherries, shrubs and trees, in North America. Two of the more common wild cherries are the chokecherry and the wild black cherry. They both grow well in moist soils.

The chokecherry is found in the northeastern United States and southcentral and southeastern Canada. It has smooth gray bark and short, rounded leaves. In spring, tiny fragrant white and pink flowers bloom. The chokecherry reaches heights of 10 to 20 feet (3-6 m.) and bears dark red, sour-tasting cherries. Birds love to eat them anyway.

▨ WILD BLACK CHERRY

▥ CHOKECHERRY

CHOKECHERRY

The wild black cherry is a much larger tree, growing to heights of 40 to 80 feet (12-24 m.). Its bark is brown with thin cracks. The wild black cherry blooms in late May or early June. Its small white flowers develop into tart purplish-black cherries loved by birds, bears, and other small mammals. This tree is found in the whole eastern half of the United States and southeastern Canada. Its cherry hardwood is a beautiful, rich dark red color and is used to make fine furniture.

WILD BLACK CHERRY

You can often look at a willow tree and see which way the wind is blowing. Its slender, graceful branches hang down and stir with the slightest breeze. Willows usually grow near water, along streams and rivers and by ponds and lakes. They have strong root systems that spread out like nets to hold soil in place and prevent soil erosion. Willows are also good shade trees and effective windbreaks.

The black willow is found in the eastern half of the United States, southeastern Canada and parts of Mexico. It often has clustered trunks and reaches heights of 30 to 60 feet (9-18 m.). The tree's bark is rough and dark brown in color. In early spring, clusters of yellowish-green flowers called catkins bloom. The female flowers later release tiny, hairy seeds. Black willow leaves are long, curved, and very narrow–only 1/8 to 3/4 inch (3-19 mm.) wide. They are a medium green color on both sides and turn yellow in autumn. With its soft, fine-grained wood, black willow timber is used to make boxes, caskets, furniture, artificial limbs, and whistles. The tree's long, thin twigs bend easily and make wonderful baskets. Willow bark also yields tannin which is used to tan leather.

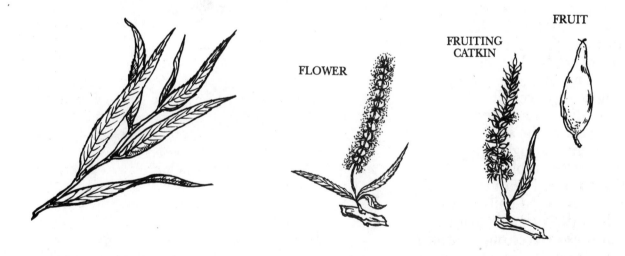

FLOWER

FRUITING CATKIN

FRUIT

There are more than 300 different kinds of willows in the world. Two of the more well-known ones are the weeping willow and the pussy willow. Weeping willow branches droop down and sweep the ground. Pussywillow shrubs and trees offer one of the earliest signs of spring. Their soft, fuzzy catkin buds feel just like the fur of a kitten.

**DECIDUOUS
LARGE**

The sweet gum, or red gum, is a tall, stately tree found in the southeastern United States and along the Atlantic coast as far north as New York and Connecticut. It grows well in moist places and is an excellent shade tree. Most sweet gums reach heights of 80 to 120 feet (24-37 m.).

The sweet gum gets its name from a sap that seeps from the tree. Hardened clumps of it, called storax, can be chewed as gum. In addition, storax is also used to make perfumes and medicines. Sweet gum wood is heavy and brown. It is used for furniture, veneer, cabinets, boats, and toys.

Beautiful star-shaped leaves, with five or seven points, grow alternately on the twigs of the sweet gum tree. They are shiny green in summer and turn a brilliant red, yellow, or purple color in autumn. The sweet gum is one of the forest's prettiest fall trees.

Sweet gum fruits are prickly balls which burst open each autumn and release small winged seeds. These seeds are a tasty treat for birds and squirrels. Throughout the winter months, the empty balls hang on the trees and look like ornaments of decoration. The bark of the sweet gum tree is gray, rough, and corky. It resembles alligator skin! With its decorative seed balls and scaly bark, the sweet gum is almost as interesting to look at in winter as it is in summer or fall!

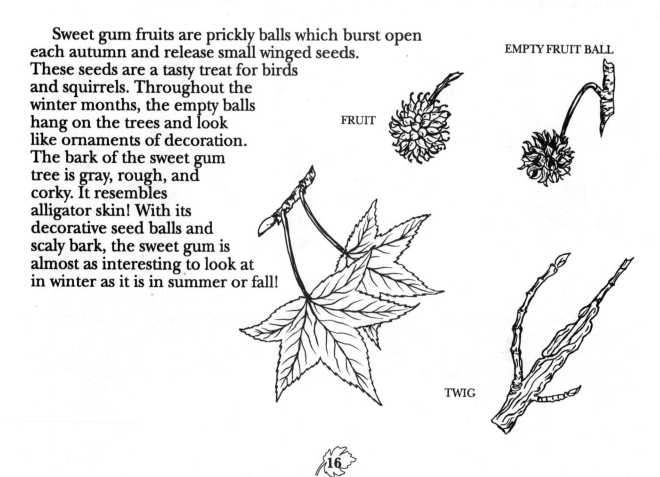

EMPTY FRUIT BALL

FRUIT

TWIG

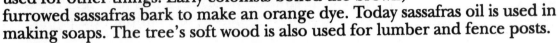

The sassafras is a tree that is good to eat! Native Americans called it Green Stick because of its bright green twigs which are tasty when chewed. Rabbits and deer enjoy them, and people do, too! A pleasant-tasting tea is made by boiling the outer bark of the sassafras tree's roots. Sassafras tea has a spicy flavor. If you crush a sassafras leaf in your hand, you will smell the tree's spicy scent. The sassafras tree is also used for other things. Early colonists boiled the brown, furrowed sassafras bark to make an orange dye. Today sassafras oil is used in making soaps. The tree's soft wood is also used for lumber and fence posts.

Sassafras trees have been around for millions of years. They are not forest trees and grow best along roads and in open fields. Sassafras trees reach heights of 30 to 50 feet (9-15 m.) and are found in the eastern half of the United States.

In spring, clusters of tiny yellow flowers appear on sassafras trees. These are followed by small purple fruits that look like berries and grow on the ends of thin stalks. Birds and black bears love to eat them. Sassafras leaves are very unusual and are a distinctive feature of the tree. They grow in three shapes—one that looks like a mitten, another that has three lobes, and a third one that is oval-shaped. The leaves are 3 to 6 inches (7.5-15 cm.) long. In autumn, they turn brilliant orange and red colors. The sassafras is one of our most colorful trees and one of the tastiest!

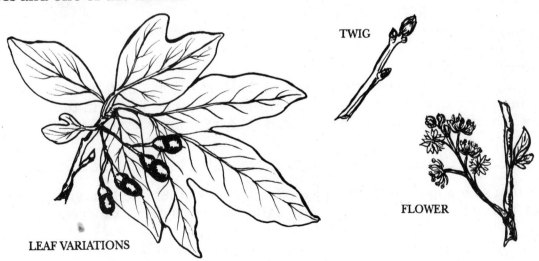

LEAF VARIATIONS

TWIG

FLOWER

EASTERN WHITE PINE

The eastern white pine tree is found throughout New England and southeastern Canada, as far south as Georgia, and as far west as Minnesota. It is the state tree of Maine and Michigan. This sturdy evergreen thrives in sandy or rocky soil and reaches heights of 50 to 100 feet (15-30 m.). Years ago, colonists used the tall, straight, branchless trunks for masts of sailing ships. Today the evenly-grained pine wood is a prime source of lumber and is widely used in building furniture, flooring, and shelving. Pine wood pulp is also used to manufacture paper.

The eastern white pine is shaped like a pyramid and, along with other types of pines, is a popular choice for cut Christmas trees.

Its leaves are soft, blue-green needles from three to five inches long. They always grow in clusters of five. The tree bears long, slender pine cones, about eight inches (20 cm.) in length, with thin, rounded scales. Seeds develop on the scales of the pine cones and, after a year or two, are ready to grow into new trees. Over the last few decades eastern white pine trees have been cut down in great quantities. Major efforts are under way to replant new stands of pines.

EASTERN WHITE PINE

BRISTLECONE PINE

Throughout the world, there are about 100 species of pines ranging from small, scrublike shrubs to trees with heights of 200 feet (61 m.) or more. Pines are the number one source of timber in the world. Bristlecone pines, found in the Rocky Mountains, are among the oldest living things on earth. Some are over 4,000 years old.

"Strange that so few ever come to the woods to see how the pine lives and grows and spires, lifting its evergreen arms to the light, –to see its perfect success...."

Henry David Thoreau
from The Maine Woods

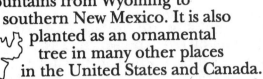

Spruces are cold weather trees. More than forty different kinds of spruces grow throughout the Northern Hemisphere, some as far north as the Arctic Circle. The blue spruce grows wild in the Rocky Mountains from Wyoming to southern New Mexico. It is also planted as an ornamental tree in many other places in the United States and Canada. It is the state tree of Utah and Colorado.

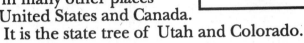

The blue spruce is best known for its beautiful bluish-green foliage. Stiff, sharp, one-inch (2.5 cm.) needles grow separately in spirals around the tree's twigs. A thick wax covering the needles gives them a silvery appearance. Each spruce needle is four-sided. If you cut through one, the cross-section will be square. Two to four inch (5-10 cm.) cones containing winged seeds hang straight down from the blue spruce branches. During the long winter when food is scarce, grouse and rabbits eat the spruce needles, and songbirds snack on the tree's winged seeds.

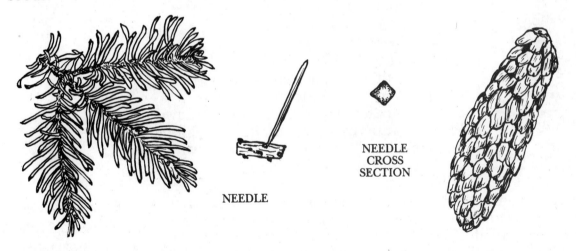

NEEDLE

NEEDLE
CROSS
SECTION

The blue spruce has a pretty pyramidal shape. It grows slowly and reaches heights of 100 feet (30 m.). Some trees live as long as 400 years! Smaller blue spruces are popular choices for Christmas trees.

Spruce wood is strong and straight-grained. It is used to make boats, boxes, sounding boards for pianos, and pulp for paper. Spruce bark is also used to produce turpentine, resin, and tannin.

AMERICAN HOLLY

For many years, sprigs of dark green holly leaves and red berries have been used to decorate houses and churches at Christmastime. Because of that association, the holly tree was once called the holy tree. Most likely the name holly is an adaptation of that original name.

There are many different kinds of hollies. Most are shrubs and grow in warm climates all over the world. The American holly is an evergreen tree found in the southeastern United States and as far north as Massachusetts. It reaches heights of 20 to 50 feet (12-15-m.). Holly leaves are glossy green and edged with sharp spines. Only the female trees bear the red berries. These berries are poisonous to humans, but are eaten by bluebirds, catbirds, mockingbirds, and other songbirds. Holly wood is a hardwood and is used to make musical instruments and furniture. The American holly tree, however, is grown mostly for its ornamental value. It is the state tree of Delaware.

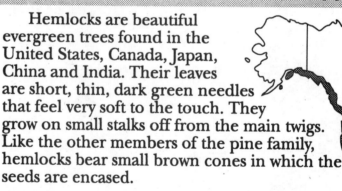

FEMALE FLOWER

HEMLOCK

EASTERN HEMLOCK

Hemlocks are beautiful evergreen trees found in the United States, Canada, Japan, China and India. Their leaves are short, thin, dark green needles that feel very soft to the touch. They grow on small stalks off from the main twigs. Like the other members of the pine family, hemlocks bear small brown cones in which the seeds are encased.

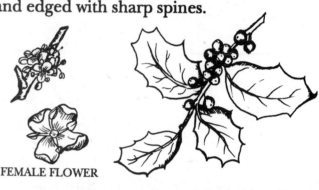

▨ AMERICAN HOLLY
▥ EASTERN HEMLOCK
▦ WESTERN HEMLOCK

The Canadian, or eastern hemlock, is the state tree of Pennsylvania and grows from the Appalachian Mountains north into Canada. This tree's bark yields tannin which is used to soften leather. The eastern hemlock grows to be 60 to 100 feet (18-30 m.) tall and is used for building frames.

The western hemlock is much bigger and reaches heights of 100-150 feet (30-46 m.). It is the state tree of Washington and grows along America's northwest Pacific coast and up through Canada. Its coarse wood is used for lumber and pulp. All of the different hemlock trees are also used in ornamental plantings.

WESTERN HEMLOCK

EASTERN HEMLOCK

20

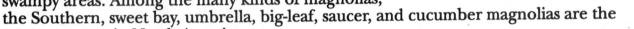

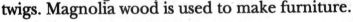

Magnolias are beautiful trees that are best-known for their large, fragrant flowers and their glossy, green leaves. There are many species of magnolias found in North America and Asia. They grow in temperate climates and range in size from small shrubs to medium-sized trees. Most are deciduous and shed their leaves when cold weather arrives; a few are evergreens. Magnolias grow well in rich, wet soils, especially along rivers and in swampy areas. Among the many kinds of magnolias, the Southern, sweet bay, umbrella, big-leaf, saucer, and cucumber magnolias are the most common in North America.

Southern magnolias grow from North Carolina south to parts of Texas and all along the coast of the Gulf of Mexico. They are evergreen trees and keep their beautiful foliage all year long. Reaching heights of 30 to 60 feet (9-18 m.), they grace the yards and gardens of many homes in the south. The Southern magnolia is the state tree and flower of Mississippi and the state flower of Louisiana. Its white, waxy flowers are 6 to 8 inches (15-20 cm.) in size–as big as a woman's hand with the fingers outstretched! They contrast beautifully with the tree's large leaves, glossy dark green on top and soft brown underneath. These leaves are 6 to 9 inches (15-20 cm.) in size and are the biggest of all evergreen leaves. In late spring, the tree's flowers give way to conelike fruits. Southern magnolias have thick branches and twigs. Magnolia wood is used to make furniture.

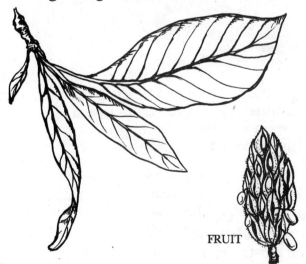

FRUIT

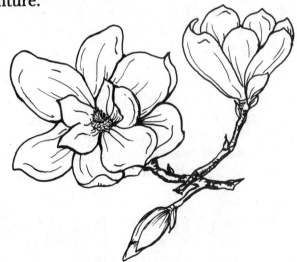

Sequoias are the giants of the plant world and are also among the oldest living things on earth. These members of the pine family grow to be between 200 and 300 feet (60-90 m.) tall! The largest tree in the world is a giant sequoia named the General Sherman Tree. It measures 273 feet (83 m.) tall and is more than 3,500 years old! Its trunk is as wide as a street! It is hard to believe that twelve million pounds of tree can grow from one tiny seed!

Giant sequoias once grew in many locations all over the United States, in Europe, and even around the Arctic Circle. But heavy lumbering severely reduced those stands. Today most of these giant trees are found only in two narrow belts in the Sierra Nevada Mountains in California. They are part of the Sequoia National Park and are protected by the U. S. government.

Sequoia wood is coarse and, because of its amazing size, was once used for heavy construction of bridges, large beams, and furniture. Its reddish-brown bark is very thick and has deep furrows. Sequoia leaves are blue-green in color and grow in sharp points all around the tree branches. The tree bears small reddish-brown cones, 1 3/4 to 2 3/4 inches (4.5-7 cm.) in length, with diamond shaped scales.

Among the earth's many trees, sequoias are considered to be in a class by themselves. Most other trees, after one or two hundred years, die from insect plagues, disease, or fungi. But giant sequoias live on and continue to grow for thousands of years. Famous naturalist, John Muir, traveled extensively in his continuing studies of nature. He wrote:

...Nothing hurts the Big Tree. I never saw one that was sick or showed the slightest sign of decay. It lives on through indefinite thousands of years...Only fire and the axe...threaten the existence of these noblest of God's trees.

REDWOOD

Redwood seeds are 1/16 inch (2mm.) long-- about as big as dashes on a typewritten page. Yet over a 500 year span, these tiny seeds grow into the tallest trees in the world! Redwood trees can reach heights of more than 300 feet (90 m.)! The tallest known redwood is called the Founders Tree and grows in Redwood National Park. It is 368 feet (112 m.) tall!

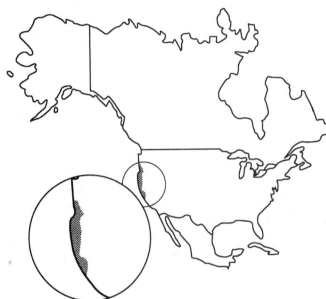

Redwoods are related to the giant sequoia trees. Like their huge cousins, they were once very common trees but now grow mostly in state and national parks along the Pacific coast in northern California and southern Oregon. The humid, moderate climate there is just what they need. Some redwoods live to be more than 1000 years old! Redwood forests are cool, shady places. Usually the trees grow so closely together that their leaves form a canopy and block out most of the sunlight.

The redwood is California's state tree. Its ridged bark can be as much as one foot (30 cm.) thick. It provides great protection from insects and fire. Redwood leaves are yellow-green needles one inch (2.5 cm.) long. Small cones the size of grapes grow at the ends of the branches. As its name suggests, redwood is red in color and is also amazingly resistant to insects and decay. It is used to build houses, indoor and outdoor furniture, and railroad ties. With more than 300 feet of timber, one redwood tree has enough wood to build four houses!

WESTERN RED CEDAR

**EVERGREEN
LARGE**

The western red cedar is one variety of cedar tree that grows from the Pacific coast to the Rocky Mountains and north to Canada and southeastern Alaska. This large tree with thin, reddish-brown bark reaches heights of 70 to 180 feet (21-55 m.). Because it has shallow roots, it grows well in moist soil. Its shiny, dark green scalelike leaves grow flat against the branches. The western red cedar also bears small one-half inch (12mm.) cones.

For centuries, cedar trees have played a rich historical role. They have long been considered symbols of goodness, power and long life. Cedar wood resists rotting better than most woods and has a pleasant smell that repels moths. Egyptian mummy cases were made from this finely-grained wood, and it is reputed that King Solomon's temple and the sacred Hebrew Ark of the Covenant were also made from cedar. The Cedars of Lebanon are mentioned more than thirty times in the Bible. Nothwest Pacific Native Americans carved totem poles and face masks from cedar and hollowed out cedar logs to make canoes. Today cedar wood is used to line closets and clothing chests and to make telephone poles, fence posts, boats, and pencils. It is also the number one wood used for roof shingles.

The baldcypress is not a true cypress at all. In many ways, it looks like the other members of that evergreen family, but it is actually related to the giant sequoia.

Baldcypresses are found in swamps or wet areas along the southeastern Atlantic coast and in states bordering the Gulf of Mexico. They grow to be 80 to 100 feet (24-30 m.) tall. Odd bumps of trunk called "knees" grow up from the trees' shallow roots, giving the baldcypresses a very broad base. Scientists think these knees may provide air for underwater roots and help support the tree to keep it from blowing over.

Baldcypress leaves are soft, light green, feathery needles similar to those of the hemlock. Each autumn, the tree sheds its leaves and also loses many twigs. This is probably how the baldcypress gets its name. In winter, the tree looks dead! The baldcypress' fruit is a small, purplish cone about one inch (2.5 cm.) around. Winged seeds are under the cone's scales.

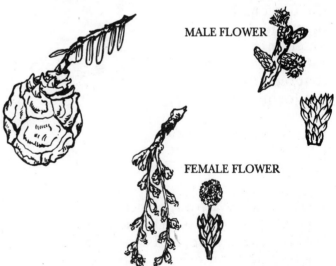

MALE FLOWER

FEMALE FLOWER

Cypress wood is light brown in color and smells like cedar. It is very durable and resists rotting. For these reasons, it is used to make railroad ties, fence posts, and is used for general construction.

The Joshua tree, or western yucca, is a strangely-shaped desert tree found in the southwestern United States and Mexico. It was named by Mormon settlers who thought the tree looked like the Biblical character Joshua with his arms stretched up toward heaven. Joshua trees are part of an ancient group of plants. Petrified Joshua wood samples as much as two million years old have been found.

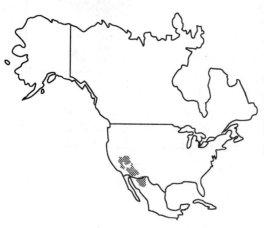

Joshua trees have scaly trunks and grow to be 15 to 25 feet (4.5-8 m.) tall. They are evergreens and do not shed their stiff, pointed, sharp-edged leaves. In March or April, tall clusters of chartreuse flowers shaped like bells bloom. These flowers are pollinated by small white moths that lay their eggs in the flowers. In turn, the eggs hatch into caterpillars that feed on the Joshua seeds.

LEAF CLUSTER

FLOWER

FRUIT

LEAF

For years, Native Americans have found numerous uses for Joshua trees and smaller yucca shrubs. The flowers and fruits are eaten by desert Indians. Baskets, mats, rope, and sandals are made from the plants' strong leaf fibers. Native Americans also use the trees' rootlets to make a red dye.

The Douglas fir is a majestic evergreen tree that stands tall above its neighboring trees in forests throughout the western United States and Canada. It grows along the Pacific coast and in the Rocky Mountains. Next to the giant sequoia, it is our largest tree. The Douglas fir grows to be 180 to 250 feet (55-76 m.) tall! It is the state tree of Oregon.

The Douglas fir is one of the world"s most valuable timber trees. It yields more lumber than any other kind of tree in North America. The wood is also used to make boat masts, posts, telephone poles, and plywood. Smaller Douglas firs make beautiful Christmas trees, too.

In dense forests, the Douglas fir's trunk is long and bare at the base. But when it grows in open spaces, its branches grow from the ground and up. The big tree is shaped so that snow slides off it easily and doesn't break the branches. The Douglas fir is not really a fir, but is related to the hemlock. Its leaves are flat , grayish-green needles that grow in a spiral around the twigs. Like those of the hemlock, they are soft to the touch. The Douglas fir bears reddish, oval cones two to four inches (5-10 cm.) in length. Tiny, three-pointed bracts, or needles, grow from each cone scale.

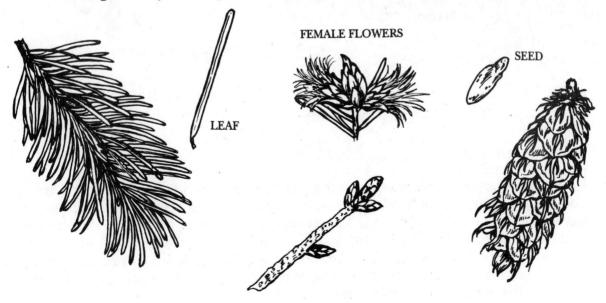

LEAF

FEMALE FLOWERS

SEED

WASHINGTONIA PALM

There are more than 2,600 types of palms. They are ancient plants that once grew during dinosaur times all over the world. Today palms are found in warm climates, especially in southeast Asia, tropical America, and the Pacific Islands. In the United States, they are found as far north as North Carolina and the deserts of California. The palmetto tree is the state tree of South Carolina, and the Sabal palm is Florida's state tree.

Palms are very valuable plants, especially to people who live in the tropics. The trees' timber and thatch are used to build furniture and houses there. Leaves and other palm fibers are made into ropes, brooms, mats, and baskets. Palm oil and coconut oil are also used in countless products such as ice cream, margarine, cooking oil, and soaps. Dates and coconuts are a few palm fruits that are popular foods.

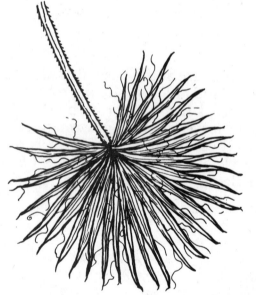

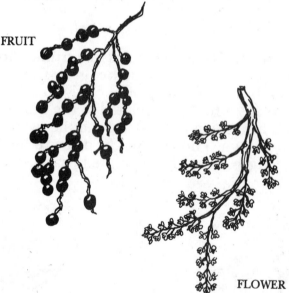

FRUIT

FLOWER

The Washingtonia palm is native to the western United States. This desert tree grows in canyons and near waterholes in southern California and Arizona. It reaches heights of 40 to 60 feet (12-18 m.). The Washingtonia palm has large, fan-shaped evergreen leaves that grow from a thick stalk. The leaves measure 4 to 5 feet (1.2-1.5 m.) across! Sometimes these leaves die and hang down from the tree, like a skirt, while new growth sprouts above. The tree's small, white flowers develop into little, round, black fruits that are edible.

HOW PAPER IS MADE

More than 4,000 years ago, ancient Egyptians used a plant called papyrus to make flat mats upon which they could write. Two thousand years later, in the first century, the Chinese discovered how to make paper from wood. The idea did not catch on, however, and for hundreds of years after that, paper was made from rags. It wasn't until the late 1700's that people once again began making paper from wood. Even then, though, it was a slow process done by hand. Because of this, paper was very scarce. Few people owned books, and schoolchildren wrote upon slates in colonial classrooms. In the years since then, the paper-making process was refined, mechanized, and computerized. Today more than 95% of the world's paper is made from the wood of trees.

Each year in the United States, lumberjacks cut down more than four billion mature trees to begin the paper-making process. First the branches are sawn off, and then the bark is removed. Bark would make dark spots in the paper. The bare logs are loaded onto flatbed trucks and taken to paper mills. There a machine grinds the wood into tiny chips almost as fine as powder.

◀ WOOD CHIPS

The paper-making machine is a huge one - as long as two football fields put together! The workers at one end of the machine can't see the workers at the other end! It is also a very hot and noisy place. A giant mixer blends the wood chips with chemicals and water to make a paste. This mixture is cooked to make to make wood pulp. At this point, the pulp looks like oatmeal!

◀ CHEMICALS

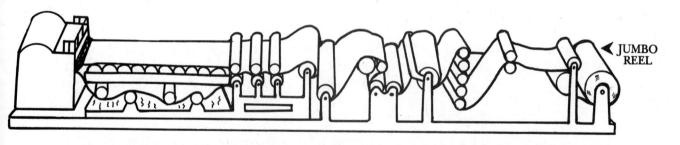

◀ JUMBO REEL

The wood pulp is poured onto a screen that acts like a sieve and drains the extra water and chemicals away. A web of wet, fibrous paper is left on the screen. Huge hot rollers squeeze this flat and press it dry. Now the paper is smooth and thin.

This finished paper is wound into giant rolls called "jumbos." They hold several miles of paper! These jumbos are shipped to factories and warehouses where they are trimmed and cut as needed to make other products.

Paper-making is a big business. The average person in the United States uses 591 lb. (268 kg.) of paper each year! Money, magazines, tickets, stamps, posters, newspapers, greeting cards, boxes, books, tissues, toilet paper, bags, envelopes, waxed paper, tagboard, napkins, wrapping paper, wallpaper, paper dolls, and many more things are made from paper. Can you think of some others?

YOU CAN MAKE A DIFFERENCE!

 80% of the trash thrown away by an average American family can be recycled.

This symbol appears on many products made of recycled materials. It also used to show that something can be recycled. If you have a choice, always choose to use an item that has been or can be recycled.

In ten years' time, more than half of America's landfills will be full. You can help by recycling as much as possible. Things made from aluminum, tin, steel, glass, and paper are recyclable. Clothing, oil, and tires can also be recycled.

 It takes about 3,000 years for a glass bottle to break down, or biodegrade, at a landfill.

Aluminum foil is durable and reusable. Use it over and over until it can't be used again. Then recycle it.

Aerosol cans, juice boxes, and squeezable plastic bottles used for ketchup, mustard, and other things are made from several different kinds of material and cannot be recycled. Try to purchase these same products in recyclable packages.

It is easy to tell whether a cardboard box, such as one used for cereal or cookies, is made from recycled materials. If the underside of the top flap is gray or dark brown, the box has been recycled. If the underside of the box is white, it is not made from recycled materials.

 The people of New York City discard enough trash each day to fill the Empire State Building!

More than 2 1/2 billion batteries are thrown away in the United States every year. Batteries contain mercury, a poisonous metal which seeps out and pollutes the environment. When you buy batteries, get rechargeable ones or, whenever possible, buy items that are solar-powered and don't need batteries at all.

It takes at least 25 years for a tree to grow tall enough to be made into paper. Yet we use that paper for only a few minutes and then throw it away!

➡ **Forty million acres of tropical rainforests – an area bigger than the state of California – are burned or cut down each year.**

➡ **If all the people in America recycled their Sunday newspapers, more than 500,000 trees each week or 26 million trees each year could be saved!**

➡ **The average American uses up 7 trees each year, in paper, wood and other items made from trees.**

When you shower, you use five gallons of water every minute. A ten-minute shower uses up 50 or more gallons of water! Take shorter showers. Install a low-flow shower head. This adds air to the water and cuts the water flow in half.

Take your own canvas bags with you when you go shopping so you don't need to use the store's paper or plastic bags.

➡ **The wood and paper that Americans throw away each year is enough to heat 50 million homes for 20 years.**

Turn off the water while you are brushing your teeth. Leaving it running can waste up to five gallons of water.

Don't leave the water running while you wash dishes either. This can waste as much as 30 gallons of water!

Use cloth towels in place of paper towels. Cloth towels can be washed and reused over and over again.

➡ **Every ton of paper that is recycled saves 17 trees.**

Each time a toilet is flushed, 5 to 7 gallons of fresh water go down the drain. Overall, one-third of the water used in most homes is flushed away in toilets. This can be changed! Fill a gallon or half-gallon plastic jug with water and cap it. Place the jug in the toilet tank so that it's not in the way of the flushing mechanism. This reduces the amount of water needed to refill the toilet tank after each flush. You will save water each time the toilet is flushed.

Almost a third of the average family's trash is made up of organic waste–biodegradable things that rot easily. Eggshells, vegetable peelings, dead leaves, grass cuttings, and many other things can be put in a compost pile. There they can decompose into fertilizer for the garden.

GLOSSARY

catkin - the soft, pointed cluster of flowers, resembling a cat's tail, that grows on willow, birch, alder and poplar trees

compound leaf - a leaf made up of two or more leaflets on a common stalk

cultivated - specifically planted and grown by people; not wild

deciduous - shedding leaves each year

drupe - a fruit whose seed is contained in a hard pit or stone surrounded by soft, pulpy flesh in the thin, outer covering. Plums, cherries, apricots and peaches are edible drupes.

evergreen - having green leaves or needles all year round. The leaves of the past season stay on the tree until new ones are completely formed.

foliage - the leaves of a plant

fruit - the part of a plant in which the seeds are. Acorns, pea pods, maple keys, cucumbers, coconuts, and apples are all fruits.

key - a dry, winged fruit. Seeds of elm, ash, and maple are contained in key fruits.

native - a plant that originated, or first grew, in that place

ornamental - a plant grown for decorative purposes

stand - a group of growing trees or plants, especially those of a particular species on a given area

tannin - the whitish acid obtained from the bark of oaks and certain other plants and used in tanning leather, dyeing, and making ink and medicines

temperate - not very hot and not very cold

veneer - a thin layer of finer wood placed over lesser wood to produce an elegant or polished surface

windbreak - a shelter from the wind or something used to break the force of the wind

wood grain - the direction or pattern of fibers and markings in wood. Wood splits along the grain.

INDEX